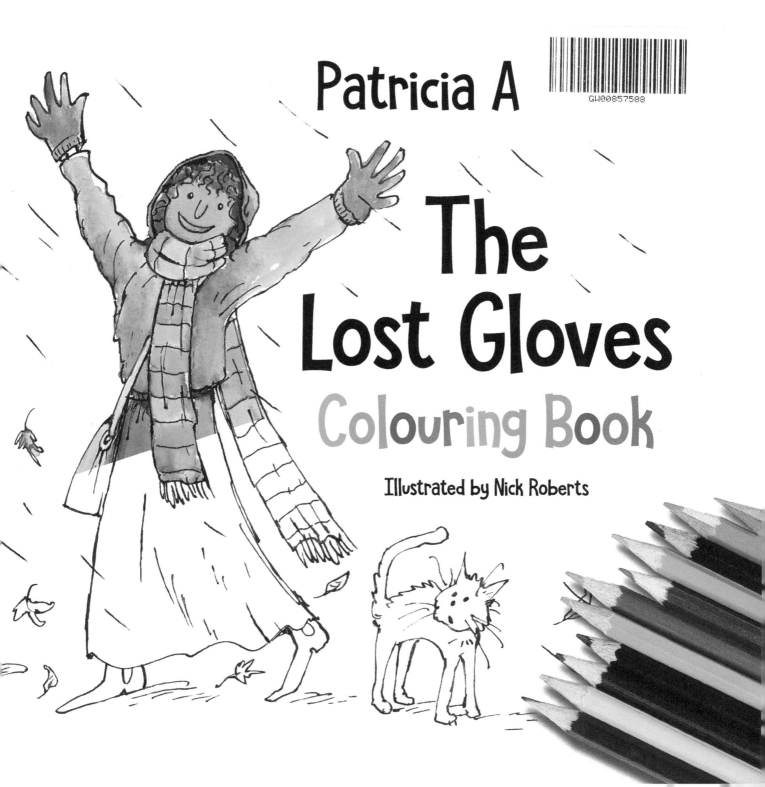

Patricia A

The Lost Gloves

Colouring Book

Illustrated by Nick Roberts

Published by New Generation Publishing in 2020

First Edition

ISBN: 978-1-80031-628-7

www.newgeneration-publishing.com

 New Generation Publishing

For Jack and Lewis

This book belongs to

....

"I think I will go shopping today and
wear my lovely warm woolly gloves."

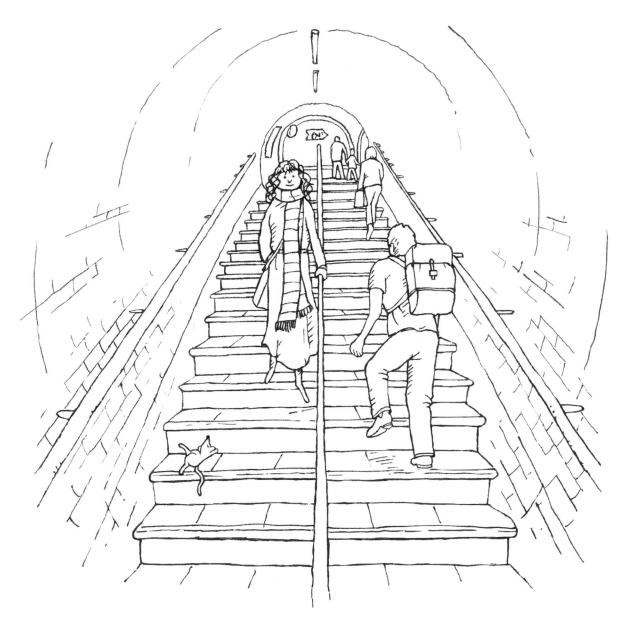

"I descended the steps onto the platform."

"I waited on the platform –
2 minutes until the next train."

Some people had to stand inside the tube
while the lucky few sat snugly in their seat.

Inside the John Lewis store an old lady said,
"Excuse me, your bag has torn open. I hope
you haven't lost anything."

"I got my steaming coffee…
I was just in time for the bus."

"OH NO! THE GLOVES ARE GONE!"

"I looked out of my bedroom window on
a rainy, cold and blustery day."

"Then an idea came to me."

"Hello, I think I lost my gloves in your shop yesterday."
"Sorry there is nothing here." Feeling hopeless Patricia
went onto John Lewis.

Patricia was taken into a room and sat down.

The waiting room had flowers on the table.

The lady was sad. She couldn't find them.
"Can you come and help me look?"

The lady and Patricia went into the lost property room and
turned the box upside down to see if they could find them.

"There they are!"

Patricia had tears in her eyes. She was so happy to find them.

Outside John Lewis, Patricia was happy that
she found her lost gloves!

What have you lost then found?

Draw an illustration and write a sentence or story about it.

Lightning Source UK Ltd.
Milton Keynes UK
UKHW051036050321
379827UK00005B/155